Arranged for all portable keyboards *by Kenneth Baker.*

THE COMPLETE
KEYBOARD PLAYER
SCOTTISH SONGS

Wise Publications
London/New York/Sydney

4.95

Exclusive Distributors:
Music Sales Limited
8/9 Frith Street, London W1V 5TZ, England.
Music Sales Pty Limited
120 Rothschild Avenue, Rosebery, NSW 2018, Australia.

This book © Copyright 1992 by Wise Publications
Order No.AM90092
ISBN 0-7119-3164-X

Designed by Pearce Marchbank Studio
Music arranged by Kenneth Baker
Compiled by Peter Evans
Music processed by New Notations

Music Sales' complete catalogue lists thousands of
titles and is free from your local music shop,
or direct from Music Sales Limited.
Please send a cheque/postal order for £1.50 for postage to:
Music Sales Limited, Newmarket Road, Bury St. Edmunds, Suffolk IP33 3YB.

Printed in the United Kingdom by
J.B. Offset Printers (Marks Tey) Limited, Marks Tey, Essex.

YE BANKS AND BRAES

Traditional

Suggested registration : harmonica
Rhythm : waltz
Tempo : fairly slow (♩ = 80)

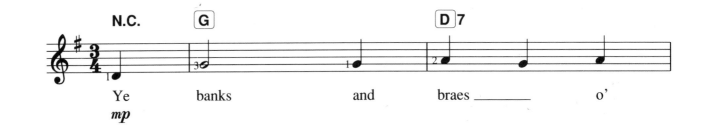

Ye banks and braes _____ o'

mp

bon - nie Doon, _____ how can _____ ye

bloom _____ sae fresh _____ and fair? How __

can ye chant _____ ye lit - tle

birds, _____ an' I _____ sae wea - ry

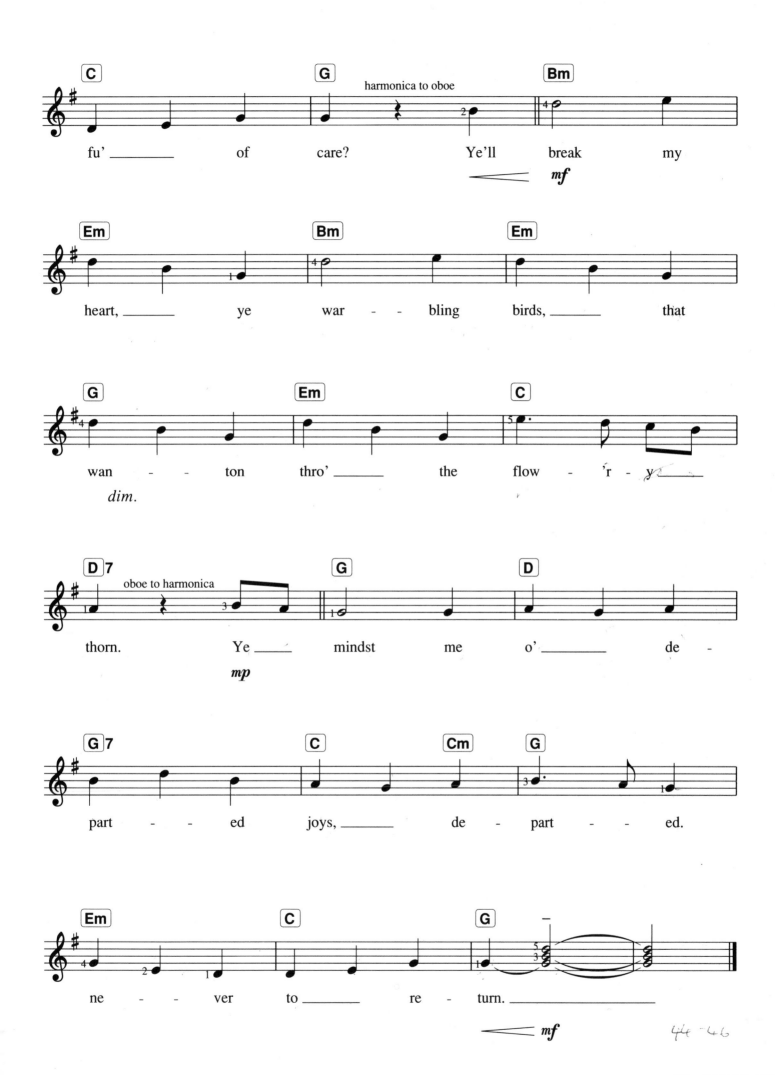

MY LOVE IS LIKE A RED, RED, ROSE

Scottish Traditional Melody
Words by Robert Burns

Suggested registration : violin
Rhythm : bossa nova
Tempo : medium (♩ = 92)

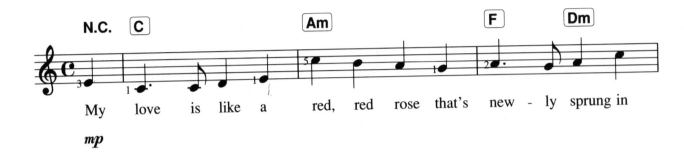

My love is like a red, red rose that's new - ly sprung in

_mp_

June. My_ love is like a mel - o - dy that's sweet - ly played in

tune. As fair art thou, my bon - nie lass, so

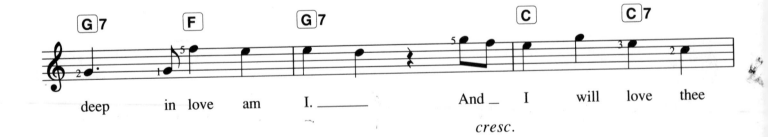

deep in love am I. _____ And _ I will love thee

cresc.

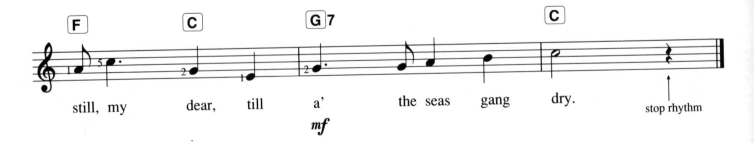

still, my dear, till a' the seas gang dry. stop rhythm

_mf_

WILL YE NO COME BACK AGAIN

Scottish Traditional Song

Suggested registration : guitar
Rhythm : 8 beat
Tempo : medium (♩ = 104)

MULL OF KINTYRE

Words and Music by McCartney & Laine

Suggested registration : flute + guitar
Rhythm : waltz
Tempo : medium (♩ = 92)

CHORUS

VERSES

1. Far have I tra - velled, ___ and much have I
2. Sweep through the heath - er ___ like deer in the
3. Smiles in the sun - shine ___ and tears in the

ANNIE LAURIE

Music by Lady John Scott
Words by William Douglas

Suggested registration : violin
Rhythm : 8 beat (or off)
Tempo : fairly slow (♩ = 88)

Max - well - ton braes are bon - nie, where ear - ly falls the _
mp

dew. ____ And it's there that An - nie Lau - rie gave

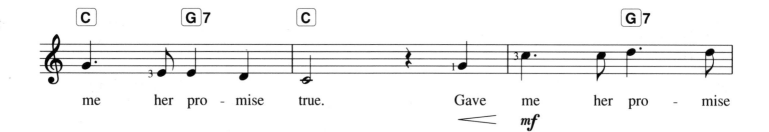

me her pro - mise true. Gave me her pro - mise
mf

true. which ne'er for - got will be. And for
cresc.   *f*   *mf*

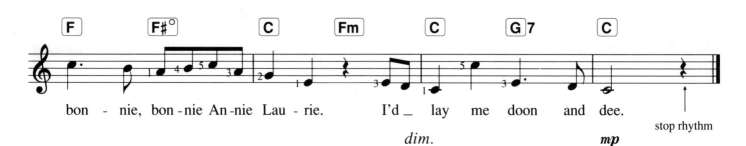

bon - nie, bon - nie An - nie Lau - rie. I'd _ lay me doon and dee.
dim.   *mp*   stop rhythm

AN ERISKAY LOVE LILT

Words and music by Kenneth MacLeod and Marjory Kennedy-Fraser

Suggested registration : harp + string ensemble
Rhythm : waltz
Tempo : slow (♩ = 76)

INTRO.

When I'm

VERSES

lone - - ly, dear white heart, black the
mu - - sic of my heart, harp of

night, or wild the sea. By love's light my foot
joy, harp of my heart. Moon of gui - dance by

(FINE)

finds the old path - way to thee. Thou'rt the
night, strength and light thou'rt to me.

(stop rhythm 2nd. time)

11

THE TARTAN

Words by Sydney Bell
Music by Kenneth McKellar

Suggested registration : accordion, to flute, to violin, to string ensemble
Rhythm : march $\frac{2}{4}$ or $\frac{4}{4}$
Tempo : fast (♩ = 184)

mf

1. There are hun - dreds of tar - tans so love - ly to
(2.) Ken - zie is no - ted, the Lind - say is
(3.) Bruce, the Bu - chan - an, the Fra - ser, and Mac -
(4.) chil - dren of Sco - tia may roam ____ the world

see, and ma - ny, a fa - mous has
grand. The Gor - don's fa - mi - liar in
-Bean. Mac - Don - ald, Mac - Mil - lan, Mac -
o'er, but their thoughts aye re - turn to the

graced the bare ____ knee. And the sett that I
ma - ny a land. And the Ca - me - ron
-pher - son and Mac - lean. But I can't name them
land ____ they a - dore. And the skirl o' the

wear is both an - cient and braw, it's the
men have a right to be proud, with the
all, and it's no use to try, so I
pipes sends the heart beat - ing high, and the

pride o' my heart, and the dear - est of
Camp - bells and Stew - arts, Mac - lead of Mac -
give you "The tar - tan from Sol - way to
tar - tans of home bring a tear to the

accordion (etc.) to brass ensemble

CHORUS

a'. Then it's hey! For the tar - tan, and
Leod. *f*
Skye."
eye.

ho! For the tar - tan. The stamp o' the

Hie - lands from Skye to Dun - dee. And it's

proud I am bear - ing the tar - tan I'm

wear - ing, the pride o' my clan, and the

1.2.3. brass to flute (etc.) 4.

tar - tan for me! *mf* me! stop rhythm

2. The Mac -
3. There's the
4. Aye! The

THE DARK ISLAND

Words by David Silver
Music by Iain MacLachlan

Suggested registration : accordion
Rhythm : waltz
Tempo : medium (♩ = 84)

VERSE

A - way to the west - ward I'm

mp

long - ing to be. Where the beau - ties of

hea - ven un - fold by the sea. Where the

sweet pur - ple heath - er blooms fra - grant and

free, on a hill - top high a - bove the dark ___

SCOTLAND THE BRAVE

Traditional Scottish Melody

Suggested registration : bagpipes (or reed)
Rhythm : march ⅔ or 𝄴
Tempo : medium 2 (♩ = 104)

INTERLUDE

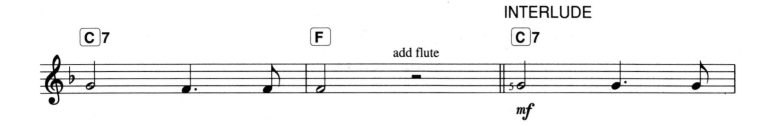

CHORUS

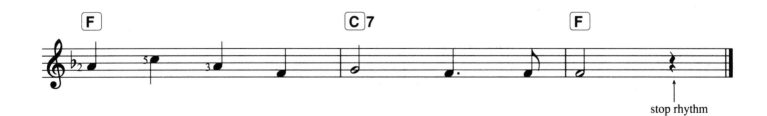

17

LOCH LOMOND

Traditional Scottish Song

Suggested registration : trumpet
Rhythm : march ⅔ or 8 beat
Tempo : medium (♩ = 92)

COMIN' THRO' THE RYE

Music Traditional
Words by Robert Burns

Suggested registration : piano
Rhythm : bossa nova
Tempo : medium (♩ = 104)

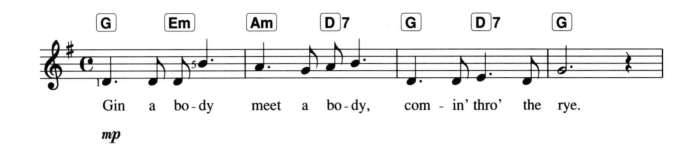

Gin a bo - dy meet a bo - dy, com - in' thro' the rye.

mp

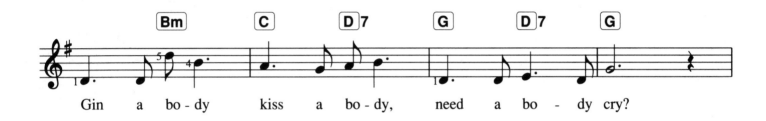

Gin a bo - dy kiss a bo - dy, need a bo - dy cry?

Ilk a las - sie has her lad - die, nane, they say, ha'e __ I. Yet

mf

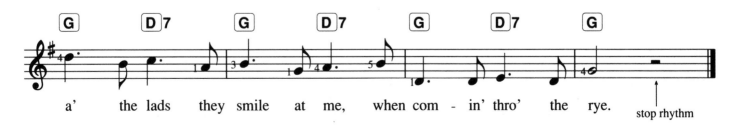

a' the lads they smile at me, when com - in' thro' the rye.

stop rhythm

DOWN IN THE GLEN

Words and Music by Harry Gordon & Tommie Connor

Suggested registration : clarinet
Rhythm : waltz
Tempo : medium (♩ = 76)

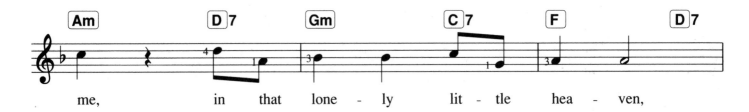

down in the glen. A - cross the moon - lit

hea - ther my las - sie calls as I roam. 'Tis

soon we'll be to - ge - ther, in that hea - ven we call

home. The sheep are in the fold, and there's

peace worth more than gold, for a shep - herd in that

hea - ven, down in the glen.

21

MARCH FROM "A LITTLE SUITE"

By Trevor Duncan

Suggested registration : harp + string ensemble
Rhythm : march ¾ (or ⁴⁄₄)
Tempo : medium 2 (♩ = 96)

INTERLUDE

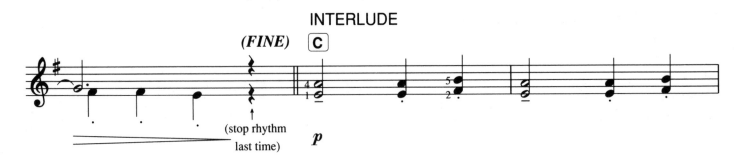

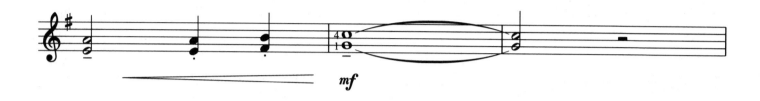

CHORUS
D.S. al FINE

23

MASSACRE OF GLENCOE

Words and Music by Jim McLean

Suggested registration : flute
Rhythm : waltz
Tempo : medium (♩ = 96)

"You are hereby ordered to fall upon the rebels -
the MacDonalds of Glencoe - and to put to the
sword all under 70." This was the treacherous
and cold-blooded order ruthlessly carried out on
13th February, 1692, when the Campbells slaughtered
their hosts, the MacDonalds, at the Massacre of Glencoe.
It was a bloody incident which had deep repercussions, and
was the beginning of the destruction of the Highlanders.

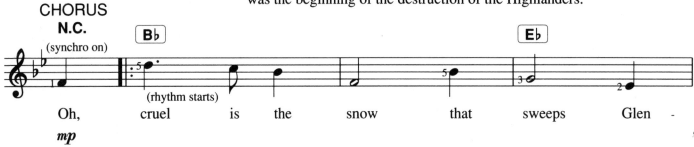

Oh, cruel is the snow that sweeps Glen -

- coe, and co - vers the grave o' Do - nald. _____

_____ Oh, cruel was the foe that raped Glen -

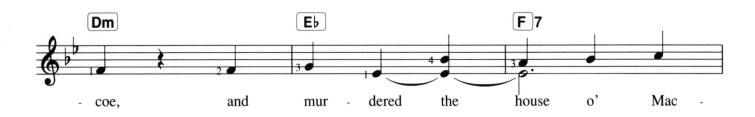

- coe, and mur - dered the house o' Mac -

THE ROAD TO THE ISLES

Words by Kenneth MacLeod
Music arranged by Patuffa Kennedy-Fraser

Suggested registration : Violin + Bagpipes (or reed)
Rhythm : swing
Tempo : medium (♩ = 104)

VERSES

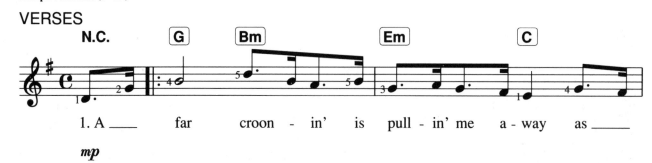

1. A ___ far croon - in' is pull - in' me a - way as ___

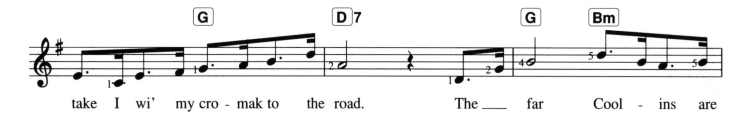

take I wi' my cro - mak to the road. The ___ far Cool - ins are

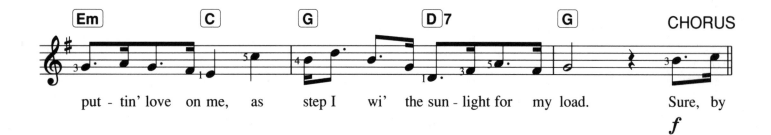

put - tin' love on me, as step I wi' the sun - light for my load. Sure, by

CHORUS

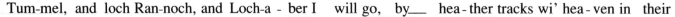

Tum - mel, and loch Ran - noch, and Loch-a - ber I will go, by ___ hea - ther tracks wi' hea - ven in their

wiles. If it's think - in' in your in - ner heart brag - gart's in my step, you've

26

nev - er smelt the tan - gle o' the Isles. Oh, the far Cool - ins are

bagpipes (etc.) to flute,
to brass ensemble
(FINE)

put - tin' love on me, as step I wi' my cro - mak to the Isles. It's by

(stop rhythm
last time) *mp*

2. It's by Sheil water, the track is to the West

By Aillort and by Morar to the sea.

The cool cresses I am thinkin' o' for pluck,

And bracken for a wink on Mother knee.

Sure, by Tummel (etc.)

3. It's the blue islands are pullin' me away,

Their laughter puts the leap upon the lame.

The blue islands from the Skerries to the Lews,

Wi' heather honey taste upon each name.

Sure, by Tummel (etc.)

THE GAY GORDONS

Scottish Traditional

Suggested registration : trumpet
Rhythm : march §
Tempo : medium (♩. = 96)

CHORUS

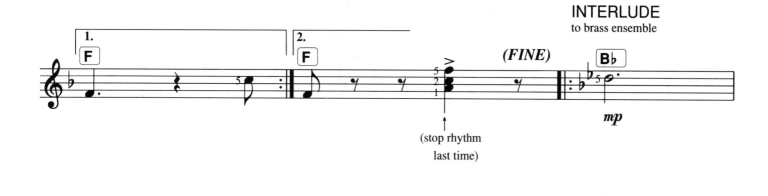

INTERLUDE
to brass ensemble

(stop rhythm
last time)

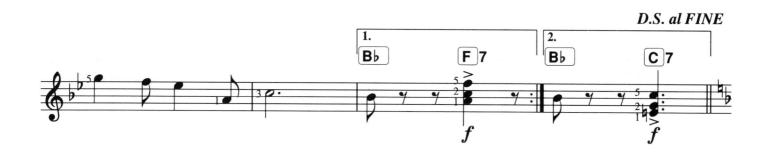

THE BLUEBELL POLKA

Music by F. Stanley
Arranged by Marion McClurg
Words by Paddy Roberts

Suggested registration : harp
Rhythm : march ³⁄₄ (or ⁴⁄₄)
Tempo : medium 2 (♩ = 76)

CHORUS

mp

Pick-in' a blue-bell in the mer-ry month of May, and
blue-bell in the mer-ry month of May, is

sud-den-ly I saw him, stroll-ing on his way. Pick-in' a
some-thing I'll re-mem-ber when I'm old and grey. And if I

blue-bell just the same as I was too, I thought I could be hap-py with a
live to nine-ty two I know darn well, I nev-er want to see an-oth-er

cresc.

(FINE)

boy like you. And as he turned and smiled at me my
Scots blue-bell!

(stop rhythm
last time)

heart stood still, I ne-ver knew a smile could give me such a thrill. He was a

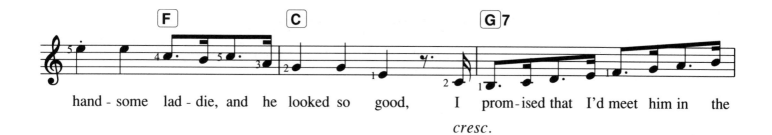

hand - some lad - die, and he looked so good, I prom-ised that I'd meet him in the

cresc.

BRIDGE

harp to flute

blue - bell wood. Half past sev - en, by the old oak tree,

f   *mf*

I was wait - ing, an - ti - ci - pa - ting what would hap - pen to a

flute to harp **CHORUS**

girl like me, when he came a - long. Pick - in' a

mp

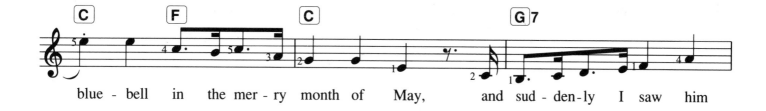

blue - bell in the mer - ry month of May, and sud - den - ly I saw him

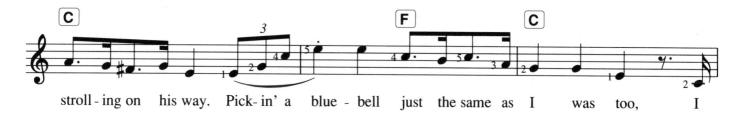

stroll - ing on his way. Pick - in' a blue - bell just the same as I was too, I

31

thought I could be hap-py with a boy like you. He looked won-der-ful,

Oh, so won-der-ful, how was I to see he would make a fool of me?

Two dark flash-ing eyes, looked like pa-ra-dise, my heart flick-ered like a

flame. What was I to do? Met my Wa-ter-loo,

there I stood for him, wait-ing in the wood for him, I'm con-fess-in' I

learned my les-son, and now I'll nev-er be the same. Pick-in' a

SKYE BOAT SONG

Traditional

Suggested registration : *piano*
Rhythm : waltz
Tempo : medium (♩ = 88)

CHORUS

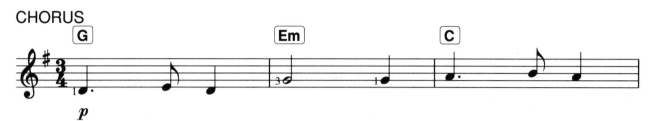

INTERLUDE
piano to string ensemble

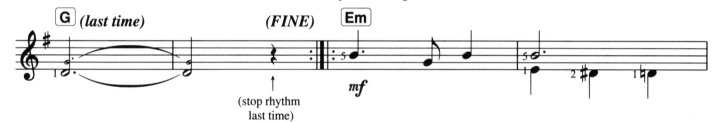

D.C. (with repeat) al FINE

SCOTTISH JIG MEDLEY

"The Campbells Are Comin'"
"Bonnie Dundee"
"Wi' A Hundred Pipers"

Suggested registration : violin (or bagpipes)
Rhythm : march $^6_8$
Tempo : medium (♩. = 104)

The Campbells Are Comin'

The Camp-bells are com-in', o - ho,   o - ho! The Camp-bells are com-in', o -

- ho,   o - ho! The Camp-bells are com-in' to bon - nie Loch Le - ven, the

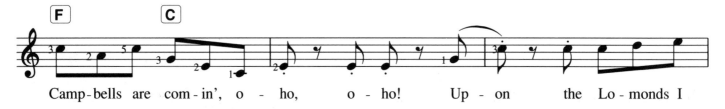

Camp-bells are com - in', o - ho,   o - ho! Up - on   the Lo - monds I

lay,   I lay. ___ Up - on   the Lo - monds I lay,   I lay. I

looked _____ down _ to bon - nie Loch Le - ven, and saw _ three bon - nie

cresc.   *f*

Bonnie Dundee

add flute

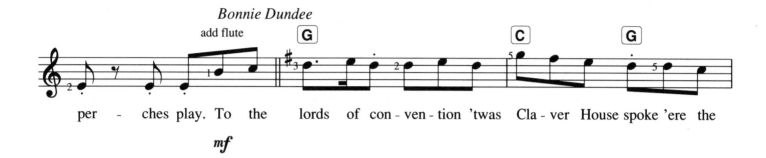

per - ches play. To the lords of con - ven - tion 'twas Cla - ver House spoke 'ere the

mf

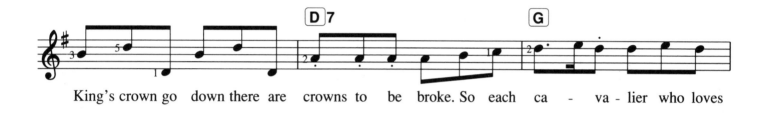

King's crown go down there are crowns to be broke. So each ca - va - lier who loves

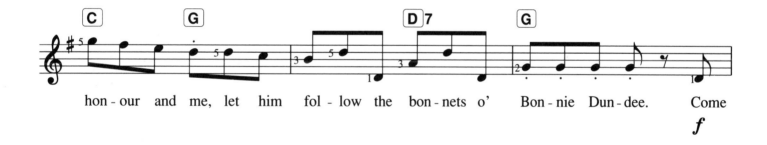

hon - our and me, let him fol - low the bon - nets o' Bon - nie Dun - dee. Come

f

fill up my cup _ come fill up my can. Come sad - dle my hor - ses, and

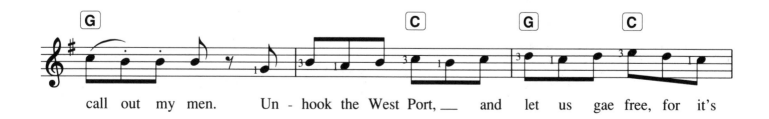

call out my men. Un - hook the West Port, _ and let us gae free, for it's

AULD LANG SYNE

Traditional

Suggested registration : trumpet
Rhythm : 8 beat
Tempo : medium (♩ = 96)

CHORD CHART (Showing all "fingered chords" used in the course)

C

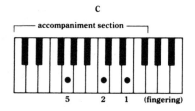

Db

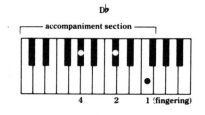

D

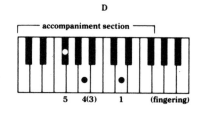

Cm

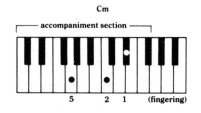

C#(Db)°

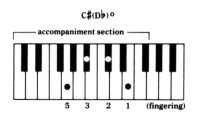

Dm

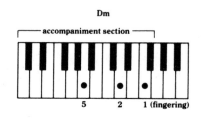

C7

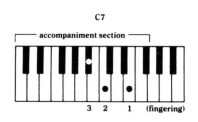

Dm7

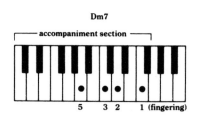

C°

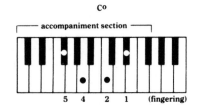

D7

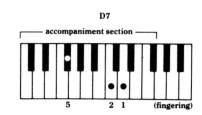

C+

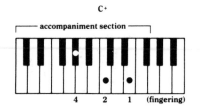

D°

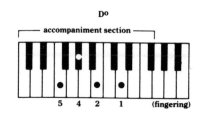

E♭

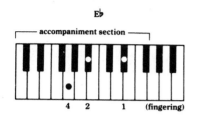

Em

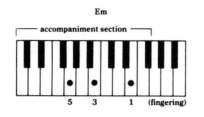

F

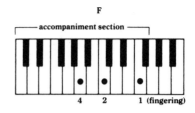

E♭m7

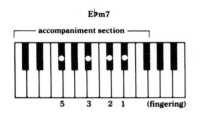

Em7

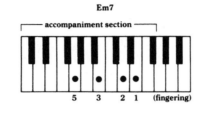

Fm

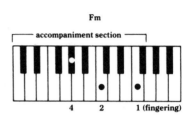

E♭º

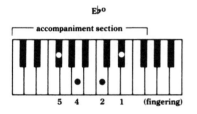

E7

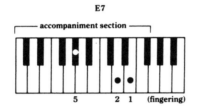

F7

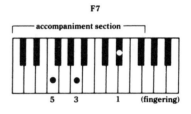

Eº

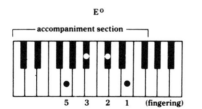

Fº

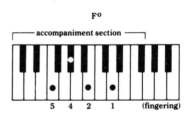

F♯º

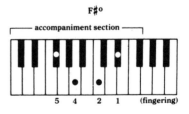

G
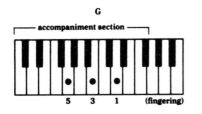
5   3   1   (fingering)

A♭
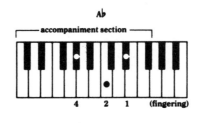
4   2   1   (fingering)

B♭
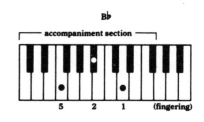
5   2   1   (fingering)

Gm
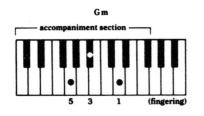
5   3   1   (fingering)

A♭7
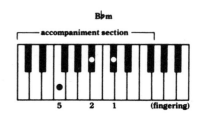
5   4   2   (fingering)

B♭m
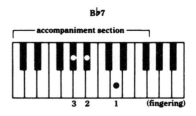
5   2   1   (fingering)

Gm7
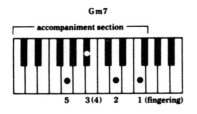
5   3(4)   2   1 (fingering)

A
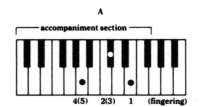
4(5)   2(3)   1   (fingering)

B♭7
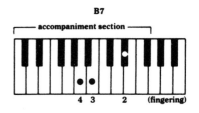
3   2   1   (fingering)

G7
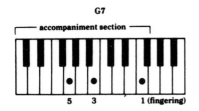
5   3   1 (fingering)

Am
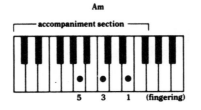
5   3   1   (fingering)

B7
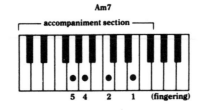
4   3   2   (fingering)

G°
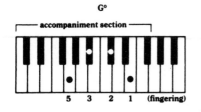
5   3   2   1   (fingering)

Am7

5   4   2   1   (fingering)

B°
5   4   2   1   (fingering)

G⁺
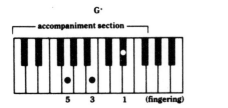
5   3   1   (fingering)

A7
5   4   2   (fingering)